Our School

I am a student at Royal Prep.

There is a headmistress at Royal Prep.

There is a dance teacher at Royal Prep.

There is a librarian at
Royal Prep.

There is a cook at
Royal Prep.

There is a gardener at Royal Prep.

Everyone helps make
Royal Prep special!